WELCOME

Welcome Scooby fans to a fun-packed! thrill-filled annual rammed full of mystery, mayhem and some seriously spooky monsters! inside there's puzzles, mysteries and some awesome activities, so what are you waiting for? Dive in and let the fun begin!

 5 The Devil and the Deep Boo Sea - Part 1

Meet The Gang! **10**

 **12** The Devil and the Deep Boo Sea - Part 2

Scooby Snacking **17**

 18 How To Draw... The Mystery Machine!

Escape From Mystery Mansion **20**

21 Witch Pitch - Part 1

Three in a Row! **26**

28 Witch Pitch - Part 2

The Unusual Suspects **33**

 34 Don't Play Dummy Part 1

Clean Machine **39**

 40 Mummy Mayhem

Don't Play Dummy Part 2 **42**

 47 Van-tastic!

Scooby Fridge Magnets **48**

 50 Curse of the Jungle Tomb - Part 1

Creepy Colouring **55**

 56 Curse of the Jungle Tomb - Part 2

Velma's Detective Test **61**

mini Mystery

Scooby's buried five Scooby Snaks for safe keeping - but now he can't remember where they are! Can you spot them all hidden in this annual?

Answer on page 61

OH! GANG, MEET MY GIRLFRIEND AND HAIRSTYLIST, *ANITA VALERA!*

NICE TO MEET Y...

MARTY, I'M SURPRISED YOU DON'T NEED SOMEONE TO INTRODUCE *YOU* TO *ME!*

MARTY AND I NEVER SPEND TIME TOGETHER EVER SINCE HE'S BECOME A SUPERSTAR...

SUPERSTAR... *¡AY DE MI!*

KIDS, I'M *CHEEKS JIMENEZ,* MARTY'S BODYGUARD. SORRY WE'RE LATE... ALL THE TIME WITH THE GIRLS AND THE NOISE!

EL REY

MAN, I MISS THE DAYS WHEN MARTY WAS TEENEE *HENRIQUE,* HUMBLE DANCER FOR THE PIN UP BAND *PECECILLOS...*

Buena Suede
Teenee...
Ronnie

THAT REMINDS ME, MY OLD PECECILLOS BANDMATE *RONALDO MORALES* IS IN TOWN! I SHOULD CALL HIM...

...BUT TODAY I'VE GOT ENOUGH FRIENDS TO RAISE THE ROOF!

THEY CALL ME *EL REY*-- *"THE KING!"*

THOSE ARE *FANS,* MARTY-- NOT FRIENDS. THERE'S A *DIFFERENCE.*

OH, HONEY, I KNOW THAT! C'MON, THIS IS THE WEEKEND WE'VE ALL BEEN WORKING FOR! LET'S DO THE FINAL *SOUND CHECK!*

GROOVY! OUR OLD PAL MARTY HENRIQUE GOES FROM BACKUP SINGER TO *INTERNATIONAL SUPERSTAR...*

IF YOUR FANS WANT SOUND AND LIGHT, THEY CAN WATCH EL ESTORBAR TERRORISE SOMEBODY ELSE. BUT NOT ME!

ADIOS, AMIGO!

I DON'T GET IT! WHILE EL ESTORBAR WAS HERE, ALL OF OUR PRIME SUSPECTS WERE IN *PLAIN SIGHT.*

AFTER ALL, BOTH *CHEEKS* AND *ANITA* HAVE MOTIVES FOR WANTING MARTY TO *FAIL!*

WE'D BETTER INVESTIGATE WHILE MARTY REHEARSES. LET'S SPLIT UP! SHAGGY, YOU'LL...

LIKE, TURN DOWN THE VOLUME ON THE *HI-FI* PLANNING, FRED!

THIS IS THE PART WHERE YOU SCOOT SCOOBY AND ME INTO SOME DUNGEON OR BAT-INFESTED TOWER, BUT OUR PAL MARTY NEEDS A *SOUND AND LIGHT DESIGNER*... RIGHT?

WELL...

AND HOW LONG HAVE I BEEN REHEARSIN' WITH *FLASHLIGHTS* AND *OCARINAS?*

RRRIGHT!

WHO BETTER TO HELP OUR *AMIGO-IN-NEED* THAN *SCOOBY* AND *SHAGGY,* THE *WIZARDS OF BEAT AND BEAM?*

WEEELLL...

...OKAY. YOU TWO HELP MARTY WHILE THE GIRLS AND I SEARCH THE AREA.

CAN YOU DIG IT, SCOOBY? WE'LL BE HIGH, DRY, AND MONSTER-FREE...

CONTINUED ON PAGE 12

Meet The Gang!

We've delved into the Mystery, Inc. filing cabinet to get you the full lowdown on Scooby and the gang!

MYSTERY INC FILE

SCOOBY DOO

Full Name: Scoobert-Doo

Nickname: Scooby-Doo, Scoob or Scooby

Age: 49 in dog years (that's 7 in human!)

Height: 12 Paws

Address: The Kennel, Shaggy's back yard, Coolsville

Key skills: Speaking and his long tail allows him to pick the locks of spooky castles and haunted mansions that need investigating!

Likes: Scooby Snacks!

Dislikes: Hunger, oh and ghosts and ghouls

Often heard to say: "Rokay!"

DID YOU KNOW?

Shaggy can spin a pizza on his finger like it's a basketball!

MYSTERY INC FILE

SHAGGY

Full Name: Norville Rogers

Nickname: Shaggy

Age: 17   **Height:** 6'0"

Address: 224 Maple Street, Coolsville

Key skills: Shaggy is the master of escape when there is a ghoul around! He even carries a pair of scissors in his back pocket so he can cut himself free if a ghost or villain grabs him!

Likes: Er, food and erm well more food

Dislikes: Anything scary!

Often heard to say: "How about a snack, Scoob?"

DID YOU KNOW?

If a creepy ghost or ghoul creeps up on Scooby whilst he's sleeping, his ears will tap his head to wake him up!

MYSTERY INC FILE

FRED

Full Name: Fred Jones

Nickname: Freddy

Age: 16   **Height:** 5'11"

Address: 123 Tuna Lane, Coolsville

Key skills: Building monster traps and is pretty skilled with a lasso

Likes: Being in the limelight and reading books

Dislikes: Being tricked by a crook or villain!

Often heard to say: "That wraps up this mystery!"

MYSTERY INC FILE

DAPHNE

Full Name: Daphne Blake

Nickname: Danger Prone Daphne

Age: 16   **Height:** 5'7"

Address: 9000 Easy Street, Coolsville

Key skills: Accidentally discovering secret passages and doorways

Likes: A mystery to solve

Dislikes: Being the damsel in distress

Often heard to say: "Jeepers"

MYSTERY INC FILE

VELMA

Full Name: Velma Dinkley

Nickname: She doesn't have one!

Age: 16   **Height:** 4'9"

Address: 316 Circle Drive, Coolsville

Key skills: Crime solving, lockpicking, dusting for fingerprints and she can speak every language in the world!

Likes: A mystery that challenges her intellect

Dislikes: Losing her glasses!

Often heard to say: "Oh no, my glasses!"

11

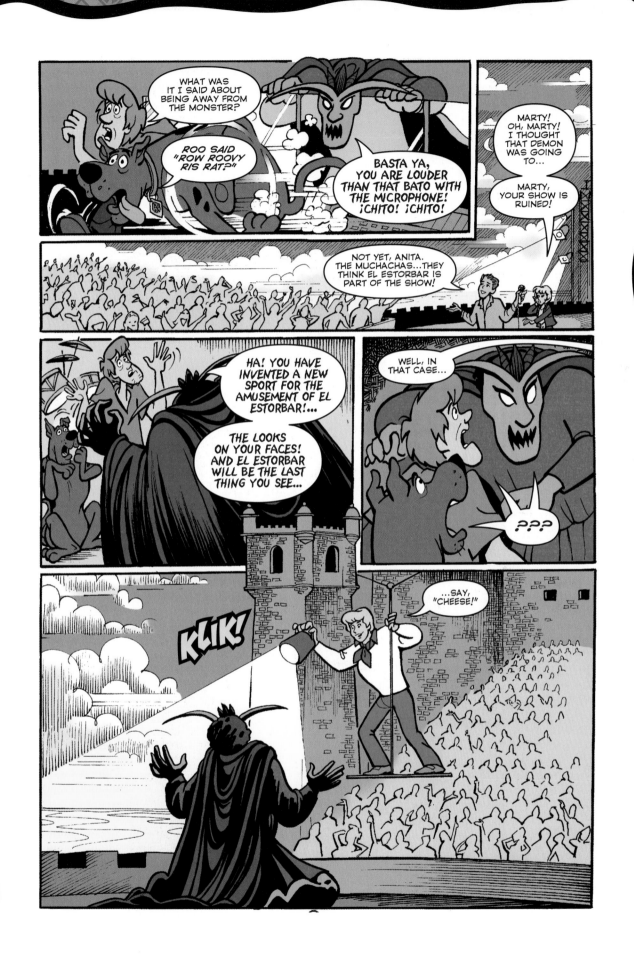

How to draw...

THE MYSTERY MACHINE!

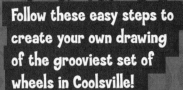

1

Use a pencil so that you can rub out any unwanted lines as you go. Start by drawing a rectangular shape with a horizontal line running through the middle.

2

Now draw in the front and rear of the van using the lines as a guide.

DID YOU KNOW?
The front of the van is based on a VW camper and the rear is modeled on a Chevrolet van!

3

DID YOU KNOW?
The van is four wheel drive which is pretty handy when trying to make a quick exit!

Add the roof, side panel detail and two circles for the wheels.

4

Rub out the outer lines and add the side window, the door detail, the roof and the wheel arches.

5

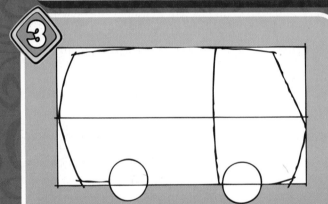

Carefully draw in the front window. Copy the wavy line that runs over the wheels. Draw two smaller circles inside the larger circles.

6

Draw in the spokes on the wheels. Now add the paintwork detail and the daisies!

DID YOU KNOW?
Shaggy and Scooby designed the logo and painted the bodywork of the van!

7

Add the roof rack, door handles and a reflection to the window. Use a black pen to draw over the lines and rub out any unwanted pencil marks. Now use your colouring pencils to add the super cool colour scheme!

MYSTERY INC FILE

THE MYSTERY MACHINE

Weight: 2.6 tonnes
Length: 14'2"
Width: 6'1"
Height: 6'2"
Top speed: 60 mph
Engine: 6 cylinder

Now follow the steps to complete the spooky scene below. We've already added the Mystery Machine logo to makes things a little easier.

Why not add some ghastly ghouls by following these steps!

ESCAPE FROM MYSTERY MANSION

Zoinks! The gang are having to make a speedy escape from The Mystery Mansion, it's overrun with phantoms! Help Shaggy and Scoob navigate thier way back to the Mystery Machine avoiding the spooky spectres!

start

THE MYSTERY MACHINE

20

· Witch Pitch ·

WELCOME TO MAIZE FIELD, HOME TO THE NEBRASKA CORNDOGS!

IT'S NICE TO BE ABLE TO SIT DOWN AND ENJOY OURSELVES INSTEAD OF CHASING AFTER GHOULS AND GOBLINS.

YOU SAID IT, DAPHNE. WE'VE BEEN SO BUSY I HAVEN'T HAD A CHANCE TO KEEP UP WITH MY FAVOURITE BASEBALL TEAM, THE NEBRASKA CORNDOGS.

THAT'S FUNNY...

...'CAUSE NEBRASKA CORNDOGS ARE MY FAVOURITE FOOD HEH, HEH.

RHEE-HEE!

THE CORNDOGS ARE ALMOST IN THE PLAYOFFS. THEY'RE TWO GAMES AHEAD OF THE CLOSEST-RANKING TEAM BEHIND THEM, THE BERMUDA TRIANGLES.

IT SAYS HERE THAT THE CORNDOGS' STAR PITCHER "SPANKY" SCHULTZ IS PITCHING TONIGHT...

...BUT THAT'S HECTOR MARTINEZ OUT ON THE MOUND.

I WONDER WHY?

HAVEN'T YOU HEARD ABOUT THE CURSE?

CURSE?

YEAH, A WITCH PUT A CURSE ON SPANKY. HE COULDN'T THROW A DECENT PITCH AFTER THAT, SO HE'S BENCHED.

THAT'S WHY THEY'RE ONLY TWO GAMES AHEAD OF THE TRIANGLES INSTEAD OF FIVE.

JOHN ROZUM · WRITER
CAMERON STEWART · PENCILLER
ANDREW PEPOY · INKER
JOHN COSTANZA · LETTER
PAUL BECTON · COLORIST
HARVEY RICHARDS · ASSISTANT EDITOR
JOAN HILTY · EDITOR

FROM THIS DAY FORWARD, HECTOR MARTINEZ, YOUR AIM SHALL NO LONGER BE **TRUE**...

...AND ANY BALL YOU THROW WILL FALL FAR AFIELD FROM WHERE YOU AIM IT!

NO!... PLEASE!

HA HA HA HA HA

MESSICK 21

THAT SINKS US!

WELL, IT LOOKS LIKE WE'LL BE CHASING A WITCH THIS TIME.

SO MUCH FOR A RELAXING EVENING!

CONTINUED ON PAGE 28

THREE IN A ROW!

Make your own Scoob-tastic three in a row game! Simply gather together all the materials you need and follow the simple instructions on the opposite page! ★ ★ Awesome!

You will need:
Newspaper, PVA glue
Scissors, Black marker pen
Ruler, Cardboard
Paints and paintbrush

1 Cut four strips of cardboard, all the same size. Cut two notches in each strip, about a third of the way across.

2 Line up the notches and fix the strips into a grid shape using sticky tape. Tape an extra strip of card to the outside of the grid to make a frame. Cover them with a layer of papier mâché and leave to dry.

3 Paint the grid light green and leave to dry. Paint black paw prints around the edge.

4 Cut ten circles from card making sure that they fit in the grid. Cut a strip of card and tape it around a circle to make a playing piece. Repeat this until you have ten playing pieces, and cover each of them with a layer of papier mâché.

5 Paint Scooby onto five of the playing pieces and Shaggy onto the other five. Paint the rest of the playing pieces black and leave to dry.

Play the game just like noughts and crosses. Pick either Scooby or Shaggy, and take turns putting one of your pieces into the grid. The first to get a row of three in any direction is the winner!

CONTINUED FROM PAGE 25

SO, HECTOR-- NEITHER YOU NOR SPANKY HAS ANY IDEA OF WHAT THIS IS ALL ABOUT?

ONLY THAT THE WITCH CURSED ME FOR FILLING IN FOR SPANKY.

AND SHE NEVER EVEN ACCUSED ME OF ANYTHING... JUST FLEW UP AND CURSED ME TO PITCH TO THE OPPOSING TEAM'S ADVANTAGE.

NOW ODIE CUNNINGHAM HERE IS THE ONLY PITCHER WE HAVE LEFT FOR TOMORROW'S GAME.

NO! NO WAY AM I GETTING MIXED UP WITH ANY WITCH! I'M JUST A ROOKIE, AND IF I BLOW THIS SEASON...

...IT'S BACK TO THE MINOR LEAGUES FOR ME!

DON'T WORRY, ODIE. I HAVE A PLAN FOR THROWING THE WITCH A CURVE BALL.

HEY, DIDN'T YOU COME IN HERE WITH SOME SKINNY FELLA AND A BIG DOG?

YEAH... HEY! WHERE DID THOSE TWO DISAPPEAR TO NOW?

LIKE, THE VENDOR SEEMS TO HAVE HEADED HOME. SINCE HE'S NOT HERE, WE'D BETTER START CHECKING OUT HIS SUPPLIES.

YOU START WITH THE PRETZELS, I'LL WORK ON THE HOT DOGS. THEN WE'LL SWITCH-HIT!

ROOD RINKIN, RAGGY. :SLURP:

THIS IS ABOUT WHERE THE WITCH MADE HER APPEARANCE. DO YOU SEE ANYTHING STRANGE?

THOSE TWO WIRES LOOK PRETTY STRANGE TO ME!

HMMM. EARLIER THIS SEASON, THEY TRIED TO RUN AN OVERHEAD TELEVISION CAMERA FROM UP THERE. BUT STOPPED USING IT BECAUSE IT INTERFERED WITH FLY BALLS.

BUT WHAT KIND OF CAMERA NEEDS A HARNESS WITH ARM-HOLES IN IT?

OUR FIRST CLUE!

AND HERE'S OUR SECOND CLUE. SOME BROOM STRAW AND A SMOKE BOMB.

DID YOU FIND THOSE IN THE SLAMMERS' LOCKER ROOM?

NO, THEY WERE IN A UTILITY CLOSET. THE SLAMMERS WEREN'T BEHIND THIS-- BUT I THINK I KNOW WHO IS!

WHO, FRED?

YOU'LL FIND OUT TOMORROW-- WHEN THE WITCH RETURNS!

OOOHHHH...

WHAT'S THE MATTER WITH YOU TWO? DID YOU DISCOVER ANYTHING?

BOY, DID WE.

DON'T EAT RELISH OUT OF A JAR WITH AN EXPIRATION DATE THAT WAS SIX MONTHS AGO.

THE FOLLOWING NIGHT...

MAIZE FIELD
HOME OF THE NEBRASKA CORNDOGS

PLAYING TONIGHT
CORNDOGS VS. ISOTOPES

IT'S THE NINTH INNING, AND THE CORNDOGS ARE ON THE MOUND AND AHEAD BY TWO POINTS. SO, IF MY HUNCH IS CORRECT...

...OUR WITCH SHOULD BE MAKING AN APPEARANCE RIGHT ABOUT...

...NOW!

ODIE CUNNINGHAM...

CUNNINGHAM
30

...LIKE YOUR FELLOW PITCHERS, I CURSE YOU TO PITCH OFF TARGET!

ZOINKS!

HA HA HA HA HA

DON'T WORRY, ODIE. REMEMBER WHAT I TOLD YOU TO DO!

GOTCHA, FRED.

HEY, PAL, WHO RETIRED AND MADE YOU THE COACH OF THIS TEAM? IT SURE WASN'T ME!

TRUST ME JUST THIS ONCE, COACH!

NOW, IF I JUST THROW HIM AN EASY PITCH THAT HE CAN'T POSSIBLY MISS...

WOOSH!

STEE-RIKE!

IT WORKED!

NOOO!!!

IT SURE DID-- AND I'LL SHOW YOU WHY.

LIKE, FRED, THERE'S GOT TO BE A CLOSER PEANUT VENDOR THAN WAY UP THERE...

ONE WITCH...

...COMING RIGHT DOWN!

THERE'S YOUR WITCH!

HEY, SHE'S HARNESSED TO THE OLD CAMERA WIRES-- SHE CAN'T FLY AT ALL! WHAT KIND OF WITCH IS SHE?

A FAKE ONE!

BUT WHAT ABOUT THE CURSE?

THERE WAS NEVER ANY CURSE. SPANKY AND HECTOR FELL VICTIM TO THE POWER OF *SUGGESTION.* IT WAS EASY, SINCE SPORTS PLAYERS ALREADY TEND TO BELIEVE IN LUCKY OR UNLUCKY CHARMS.

LIKE EATING ONLY CHICKEN ON THE DAY OF A GAME, OR SPITTING ON YOUR HANDS BEFORE GOING TO BAT.

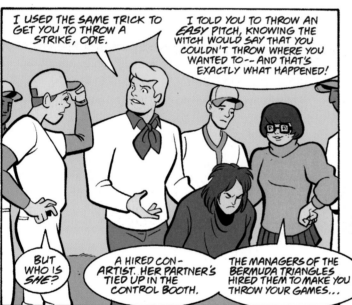

I USED THE SAME TRICK TO GET YOU TO THROW A STRIKE, ODIE.

I TOLD YOU TO THROW AN *EASY* PITCH, KNOWING THE WITCH WOULD SAY THAT YOU COULDN'T THROW WHERE YOU WANTED TO-- AND THAT'S EXACTLY WHAT HAPPENED!

BUT WHO IS *SHE?*

A HIRED CON-ARTIST. HER PARTNER'S TIED UP IN THE CONTROL BOOTH.

THE MANAGERS OF THE BERMUDA TRIANGLES HIRED THEM TO MAKE YOU THROW YOUR GAMES...

...SO *THEY'D* BE IN THE PLAYOFFS INSTEAD OF YOU.

IT WOULD HAVE WORKED, TOO, IF YOU MEDDLING KIDS HADN'T COME ALONG.

IT'S A GOOD THING YOU *DID* COME ALONG. ODIE WAS THE LAST PITCHER WE HAD.

WELL, IT LOOKS LIKE YOU JUST SIGNED UP A NEW ROOKIE!

HA HA HA HA

THE END

THE UNUSUAL SUSPECTS!

Help Velma crack this mystery! One of these crooks set all the rides at the fairground to auto pilot! Crack the clues to work out which rogues have an alibi!

Dracula   Funland Robot   Redbeard   Snow Ghost   Alien

Write down your answer in the box below when you have cracked the clues!

CLUES

1 It can't be this blood sucking nasty, he was at home in his Transylvanian castle!

2 Look! Something out of this world has left behind some footprints far away from the fairground. But who do they belong to?

4 This crook was too busy burying his loot at a secret cove on Skull Island. He's left behind some vital clues as to his identity though!

3 Ah-huh, a photo of Scoob skiing in another country, but look closer. Can you see which chilling ghoul is lurking in the background?

So you have eliminated all the crooks that were up to mishchief elsewhere, the crook that set all the rides at the funfair to autopilot is...

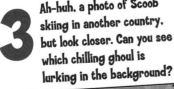

ANSWER: Funland Robot

33

SOMEBODY MADE OFF WITH ALL MY *PAYROLL MONEY*. THE FUTURE OF MY *TRAVELLING CIRCUS* WAS IN THAT SAFE! AND ON TOP OF THAT, MY *STAR ATTRACTION* DISAPPEARS!

WHEN DID SAL LASPARIE DISAPPEAR, MR. McLOONEY?

MAYBE *HE* STOLE THE MONEY AND *RAN AWAY?*

LAST TIME ANYONE SAW SAL WAS SOMEWHERES BETWEEN *HERE* AND OUR *LAST* CITY. I KNOW HE DIDN'T TAKE THE MONEY AND RUN-- HE *COULDN'T* HAVE!

ER-- WHY IS THAT?

WELL, FIRST OFF, 'CAUSE HE DIDN'T HAVE NO *LEGS*. HE'S THE *LEGLESS VENTRILOQUIST*-- THAT'S HIS *CLAIM* TO *FAME!*

AND THE *SECOND* REASON?

Don't play DUMMY with me!

Sal & Boris
TONIGHT!

SECOND REASON IS, HE LEFT HIS *PARTNER* BEHIND-- AND HE WOULDN'T HAVE GONE NOWHERE WITHOUT *BORIS!*

ROBBIE BUSCH - WRITER
VINCENT DEPORTER - ARTIST
TOM ORZECHOWSKI - LETTERER
PAUL BECTON - COLORIST
DIGITAL CHAMELEON - SEPARATIONS
HARVEY RICHARDS - ASSISTANT EDITOR
JOAN HILTY - EDITOR

THEY WAS... *CONNECTED...* YA KNOW WHAT I MEAN?

SO, YOU DON'T THINK HE WAS INVOLVED IN THE ROBBERY?

HE WAS AN ODD DUCK--BUT HE WAS A HARD-WORKIN', HONEST MAN.

AND I KNOW HE COULDN'T SURVIVE WITHOUT BORIS. THEY WAS LIKE TWO PARTS OF THE SAME PERSON.

THAT MAY BE, BUT WE CAN'T RULE OUT ANY SUSPECTS JUST YET.

AND WE'LL HAVE TO TALK TO *ALL* OF YOUR EMPLOYEES.

LIKE, CAN I SEE BORIS? I'M PRETTY GOOD AT THROWING MY VOICE!

NO! HE'S A FRAGILE PIECE OF EQUIPMENT, NOT A *TOY!*

LIKE, SORRY, MAN!

THAT'S ALL RIGHT, SON... I GUESS WE'VE JUST COME TO THINK OF BORIS AS A PART OF THE FAMILY.

SNIFF SNIFF

RIKES!

RET ME OUTTA RERE!

CRASH!!!

HEY-- OOF!

RUH-ROH!

SORRY ABOUT THAT-- SCOOBY GETS A LITTLE *OVEREXCITED* SOMETIMES.

HUMPH! *WHAT* ARE YOU CHILDREN DOING BACK HERE?!

WELL, BECAUSE...

THEY'RE HERE BECAUSE I *ASKED* 'EM TO BE, MERTRON!

I SEE YOU HAVE THAT UGLY WOODEN *MONSTER!*

TOO BAD HIS DADDY DIDN'T *TAKE* HIM WHEN HE *ROLLED AWAY* FROM HERE!

CONTINUED ON PAGE 42

Clean Machine!

The gang love nothing more than to give the Mystery Machine a good old scrub! Can you solve this picture puzzler?

a b c d

1 2 3 4 5 6

Find the image in the picture above and record the grid reference in the box below! Here's an example!

a, 6

D6

2 a c

3

4

5

6

39

MUMMY MAYHEM!

ZOINKS!
Mystery inc. have discovered a spooky Egyptian tomb. Can you spot all the objects in this creepy pyramid puzzler?

TICK AS YOU FIND...

- 4 camels _____ ✓
- 2 yellow snakes _____ ✓
- A mummified cat _____ ✓
- 3 Herons _____ ✓
- 3 Hungry alligators _____ ✓
- A buried mummy _____ ✓
- A mummified snake _____ ✓
- An aligator hieroglyph _____ ✓
- All 5 members of _____ ✓
  Mystery inc.

THE KING'S CHAMBER

THE TREASURE ROOM

ALLIGATOR POOL

40

A 'GREAT' PYRAMID

TRAPDOOR

SECRET PASSAGES

SECRET STAIRWELL TO THE TOMB

SNAKE PIT

CONTINUED FROM PAGE 38

Er... DON'T WORRY...LIKE, WE'LL GET TO THE BOTTOM OF THIS...

SHE CAN BE SO EMOTIONAL. ≈SMOOCH≈

AND WHO'S THE ONE THAT CRIED AT THE END OF CASABLANCA?

WHERE IS HE?!!

WHAT HAVE YOU DONE WITH BORIS?!

I WOULDN'T TOUCH THAT TOOTHPICK!

IT MAKES ME SICK JUST TO THINK ABOUT IT!

EASY, FELLAS! NOW WHAT'S GOING ON?

NOW BORIS IS GONE--AND MERTRON WAS SNEAKING AROUND MY TRAILER JUST BEFORE HE WENT MISSING!

I WAS ON MY WAY BACK TO MY TRAILER. I FIND BORIS REPULSIVE AND WOULD NEVER TOUCH IT!

DAPHNE AND VELMA--TAKE THE VAN TO THE LAST PLACE THE CIRCUS STOPPED.

SHAGGY AND SCOOBY WILL COMB THE MIDWAY FOR BORIS!

LIKE, I FEEL LIKE A DUMMY LOOKING FOR A DUMMY IN A HAYSTACK!

ROOK!

OOOH... WHY'D YA KNOCK ME ON THE HEAD SO HARD?! YA BIG...

uh-oh.

...AW, NUTS!

NOW LOOK WHAT YA DID, RALPHY BOY!!! IT WAS SUCH A SIMPLE PLAN!

I KNEW IT! I KNEW IT! I HAD MY EYE ON YOU, YOU... PUPPET PRETENDER!

AW, BLOW IT OUT YER FLOPPY HAT, YA BIG WINDBAG!

I-I-I...!

YOU MUST HAVE KNOWN ABOUT THIS-- YOU HIRED THE ACT! YOU AND BORIS WERE IN ON THE PAYROLL ROBBERY TOGETHER!

SO, WHEN MERTRON GOT SUSPICIOUS, THEY GOT NERVOUS AND DECIDED TO MAKE SAL "DISAPPEAR."

YES-- AND NOW IT'S TIME FOR THEM TO DO A DISAPPEARING ACT!

SPEAKING OF DISAPPEARING... WHERE ARE SHAGGY AND SCOOBY?!

LIKE, I JUST HEARD A STRANGE SOUND IN THE COTTON CANDY MACHINE AND HAD TO INVESTIGATE!

WHAT SOUND?

ROOBY-ROOBY-ROOOOOO!

THE END

Van-Tastic!

Play this groovy game with a friend to see who can load the Mystery Machine first!

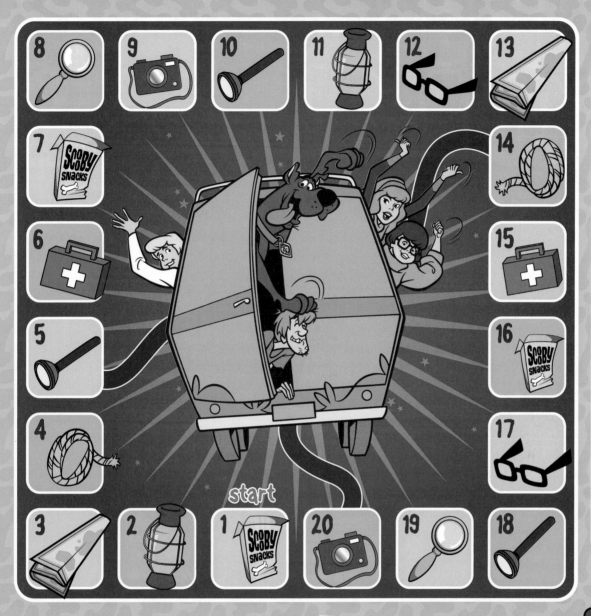

Board squares:

8 · 9 · 10 · 11 · 12 · 13

7 (Scooby Snacks) · 14

6 (First aid kit) · 15 (First aid kit)

5 (Torch) · 16 (Scooby Snacks)

4 (Rope) · 17 (Glasses)

3 · start · 2 (Lantern) · 1 (Scooby Snacks) · 20 (Camera) · 19 (Magnifying glass) · 18 (Torch)

Make some counters

Copy the pictures above, add some colour and then carefully cut them out!

Player One Checklist

Torch _____ ✓

Map _____ ✓

Camera _____ ✓

Ropes _____ ✓

Magnifying glass _____ ✓

Lantern _____ ✓

Scooby snacks _____ ✓

Velma's spare glasses _____ ✓

First aid kit _____ ✓

Player Two Checklist

Torch _____ ✓

Map _____ ✓

Camera _____ ✓

Ropes _____ ✓

Magnifying glass _____ ✓

Lantern _____ ✓

Scooby snacks _____ ✓

Velma's spare glasses _____ ✓

First aid kit _____ ✓

★ Rules ★

Throw a dice to see who goes first. Take it in turns to move around the board. Cross off the items on your checklist as you land on the squares. You can only progress up the path towards the van once you have ticked off all the objects on your checklist!

AH, THIS IS THE LIFE!

THE ONLY MYSTERY I PLAN TO FINISH THIS HOLIDAY IS THE ONE I'M READING.

BUFFET!

ALL YOU CAN EAT

RALL ROU RAN EAT!

YEP, IT'S ALL YOU CAN EAT, SO THAT MAKES IT A WORKING HOLIDAY FOR US-- EH, SCOOBY?

I KNOW I'M WORKING UP AN APPETITE!

:REE-HEE-HEE:

MMMM. REPPERS!

NO! NO! NO! WAIT, THOSE PEPPERS ARE VERY HOT!

RELAX. SCOOBY LOVES SPICY FOOD. BESIDES, THE GREEN ONES CAN'T BE HOT-- RIGHT, SCOOB?

RIGHT, SCOOB?

ROT SO HOT.

LOOK! SOMEONE'S COMING OUT OF THE JUNGLE -- AND HE LOOKS HURT!

WHO ARE YOU? CAN YOU TELL US WHAT HAPPENED?

I-I'M PROFESSOR QUATERMASS. I'M AN *ARCHEOLOGIST*.

I WAS EXAMINING SOME MAYAN RUINS OUT IN THE JUNGLE, WHEN MY TEAM AND I WERE *ATTACKED*.

ATTACKED?! ATTACKED BY WHAT?

BY A *BALAM*.

PROFESSOR! ARE YOU OKAY? WE FOUND EVERYONE BUT YOU!

A BALAM? WHAT'S A BALAM?

MY STUDENT MARIA HERE CAN TELL YOU.

A BALAM IS A *SPIRIT CREATURE* -- HALF MAN AND HALF JAGUAR.

I TRIED TO WARN HIM, BUT HE WOULDN'T LISTEN. THIS CREATURE IS--

-- THE CURSE OF THE JUNGLE TOMB!

JOHN ROZUM -writer
JOE STATON -penciller
DAVE HUNT -inker
JOHN COSTANZA -letterer
PAUL BECTON -colorist
HARVEY RICHARDS -asst. editor
JOAN HILTY -editor

CONTINUED ON PAGE 56

CREEPY COLOURING!

Go wild with your colouring pencils and add a splash of colour to this spooky scene!

CONTINUED FROM PAGE 54

LOOK! SOMEONE'S UP THERE!

RIS IT RHE RAGUAR RIEST?

HE'S NOT GOING TO TAKE OUR BLOOD, IS HE?!

THAT'S THE BALAM!

ZOINKS!

RA-OW!!!

NO, THERE HASN'T BEEN A PRIEST LIKE THAT FOR CENTURIES...

RAAOOO- OOWWW

RUN!

THE JAGUAR IS ATTACKING!

WAIT, COME BACK!

LIKE, I THINK THEY HAVE THE RIGHT IDEA, RUN, SCOOB!

RIGHT REHIND ROU!

SCOOBY! SHAGGY! WAIT!

THAT LEADS INTO THE TOMB ITSELF! THERE'S NO WAY OUT!

WELL, IT HAS TO BE SAFER THAN OUT HERE WITH THE JAGUAR!

LET'S GO, GANG!

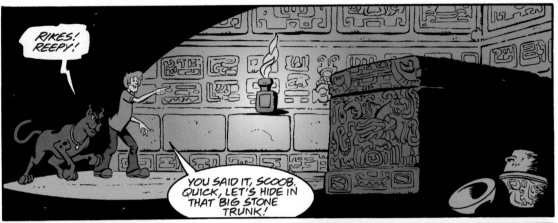

RIKES! REEPY!

YOU SAID IT, SCOOB. QUICK, LET'S HIDE IN THAT BIG STONE TRUNK!

ZOINKS! IT LOOKS LIKE THIS HIDING SPACE IS ALREADY SPOKEN FOR!

RELETON!

ZOINK ZOINKS ZOINKS

THAT SOUNDED LIKE SHAGGY!

BUT WHICH WAY DID IT COME FROM? WE'D BETTER SPLIT UP.

VELMA, YOU AND DR. GUITERREZ GO TO THE RIGHT, DAPHNE AND I WILL TAKE THE LEFT!

HMMM.

MEW

FRED, DID YOU HEAR THAT?

IT SOUNDS LIKE IT CAME FROM ONE OF THOSE CHAMBERS AHEAD.

NOTHING THERE, LET'S HAVE A LOOK AT DOOR NUMBER TWO...

RA-OW!!

YIKES!!!

YIKES YIKES YIKES

THAT SCREAM MUST MEAN FRED AND DAPHNE FOUND THE JAGUAR, WHICH MEANS THAT YOU AND ME ARE PERFECTLY--

--SAFE. GULP

RRRR

PHOOF

RUH-ROH, RAGGY.

OOF

CRASH!

BUMP!

CLONG!

ZOINKS! THE JAGUAR'S GOT ME, SCOOB!

REE TOO! RELP!

RAGGY?

LIKE, IF YOU'RE NOT THE JAGUAR, THEN WHO ARE WE SITTING ON?

ME, HELP ME FIND MY GLASSES BEFORE SOMEONE STEPS ON THEM!

LOOK! THE OTHERS CAPTURED THE JAGUAR!

IT LOOKS LIKE YOU CAPTURED A COUPLE OF YOUR OWN.

THEY'RE CUBS! THEY WERE ALL ALONE IN A CHAMBER AT THE OTHER END OF THE CORRIDOR.

AT LEAST YOURS ARE REAL. LET'S SEE WHO THE FAKE JAGUAR REALLY IS.

MARIA MARQUEZ! YOU'RE THE ONE WHO KEPT TRYING TO GET THE PROFESSOR TO ABANDON THIS SITE!

HOW DID YOU KIDS KNOW THE JAGUAR WAS A FAKE?

THE FAKE JAGUAR WAS WEARING AZTEC COSTUMING. THESE ARE MAYAN RUINS--TWO ENTIRELY DIFFERENT CULTURES!

I DID IT FOR THEM. THIS TOMB IS RIGHT IN THE MIDDLE OF A HABITAT OF REAL JAGUARS.

IF YOU BUILD THAT ROAD FOR TOURISM, IT WILL ONLY DESTROY MORE OF THEIR HABITAT. I HOPE YOU'LL THINK TWICE ABOUT IT NOW.

MEW

MEW

LIKE, HEY!

IT LOOKS LIKE SHAGGY SHARES YOUR FEELINGS FOR THE JAGUAR CUBS, MS. MARQUEZ.

KIDS! KIDS! LIKE, ONE AT A TIME!

HA HA HA HA

The End

Velma's Detective Test!

Good detectives are always paying attention super sleuths! Were you paying attention during the the comic strips in this annual?

1 The Devil and the Deep Boo Sea

Which photo was Cheeks Jimenez really holding?

A

B

C

2 Witch Pitch

Here's that crooked witch! Can you spot one thing we've changed about her?

_ _ _ _ _ _ _

_ _ _ _ _ _ _

_ _ _ _ _ _ _

3

Take a close look at this scene. Can you spot 5 things that look out of place?

WHICH WITCH?
WITCH?
THAT WITCH!
ZOINKS!

4 Don't Play Dummy With Me!

Who are the two shadowy characters?

Shaggy

Scooby

Velma

Fred

Daphne

5 The Curse of the Jungle Tomb!

Can you spot 4 things in this scene that don't belong there?